# How many cupfuls?

**1** Colour how many cupfuls each jug holds.

| cupfuls | Jug A | Jug B | Jug C | Jug D |
|---|---|---|---|---|
| 10 | | | | |
| 9 | | | | |
| 8 | | | | |
| 7 | | | | |
| 6 | | | | |
| 5 | | | | |
| 4 | | | | |
| 3 | | | | |
| 2 | | | | |
| 1 | | | | |

Date

**2:14 Volume and Capacity (1)**
Constructing a block graph to show capacity
using non-standard units.

**2**

# Cross-outs

3 Cross out the shapes that

**1** Cross out the shapes that are different in each set.

> The first one is done for you.

**2** Write the number sentences.

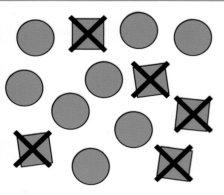

| 13 | − | 5 | = | 8 |

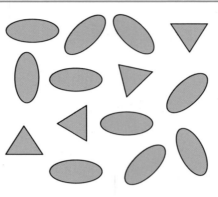

☐ − ☐ = ☐

☐ − ☐ = ☐

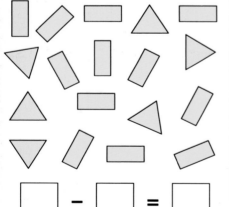

☐ − ☐ = ☐

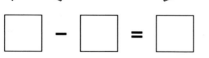

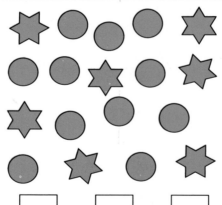

☐ − ☐ = ☐

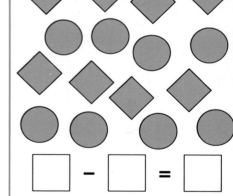

☐ − ☐ = ☐

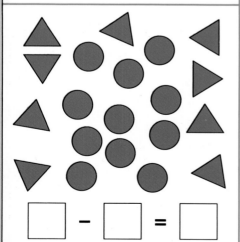

☐ − ☐ = ☐

**3** Draw your own cross-outs.

☐ − ☐ = ☐

☐ − ☐ = ☐

| Date |

Drawing and colouring materials

**2:15 Subtraction 0 – 20 (1)**
Take away, using objects, involving numbers no greater than 20.

# Smaller and smaller

**1** Use cubes to make a rod which matches this:

There are ☐ cubes altogether.

**2** Take away cubes to make the rod like this:

☐ take away ☐ leaves ☐ .    ☐ – ☐ = ☐

**3** Take away more cubes to make the rod like this:

☐ take away ☐ leaves ☐ .    ☐ – ☐ = ☐

**4** Take away more cubes to make the rod like this:

☐ take away ☐ leaves ☐ .    ☐ – ☐ = ☐

The difference between 18 and 2 is ☐ .

# Going shopping

| 10p  | 5p  | 8p  | 2p |
|---|---|---|---|
| felt-tip pen | lollipop | rubber | sweet |

**1** Complete this table.

| You buy these things | You pay | Total |
|---|---|---|
| felt-tip pen and sweet | 10p + 2p | 12p |
| felt-tip pen and marble | | |
| sweet and whistle | | |
| pencil sharpener and whistle | | |
| rubber and lollipop | | |

Date

Rubber-stamp, plastic
or self-adhesive coins

| **4p** | **4p** | **18p** | **15p** |
|---|---|---|---|
| 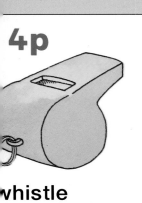 |  |  |  |
| whistle | marble | toy car | pencil sharpener |

## Coins you pay with

**2:17 Money (1)**
Using coins to calculate amounts totalling up to 20p.

6

# How much change?

**1** Buy each item with a 20p coin.

**2** Choose coins to **show the change** for each buy.

| | |
|---|---|
| **15p** | |
| **13p** | |
| **16p** | |
| **14p** | |
| **11p** | |
| **9p** | |

Date

Rubber-stamp, plastic
or self-adhesive coins.

**2:17 Money (1)**
Calculating change from 20p.

# Predict and draw

Celia's book balances
12 bricks.

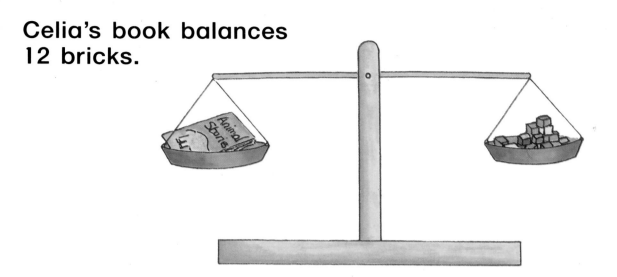

**What if Celia
took away
4 bricks?**

**1** Draw a picture
of how the
scales would
look.

**What if Celia
then added
8 more bricks?**

**2** Draw a picture
of how the
scales would
look.

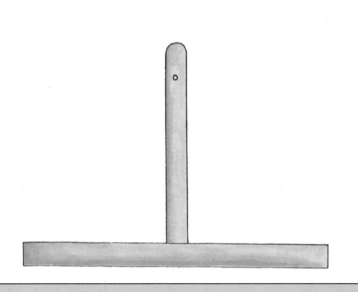

Date

Colouring materials

**2:18 Weight (1)**
Understanding the use of balance-scales with
non-standard units.

# Weight graph

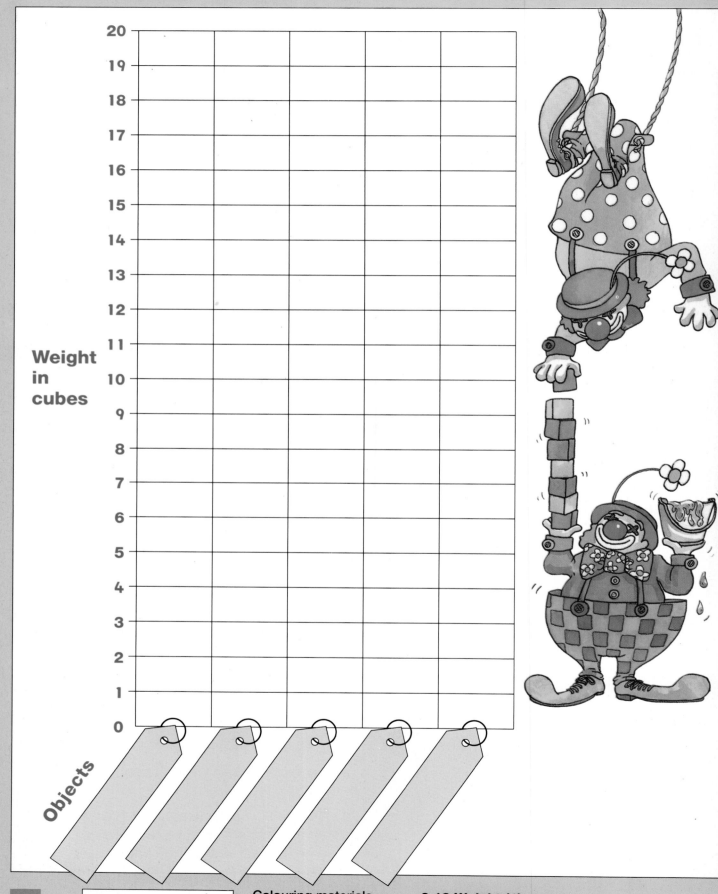

20
19
18
17
16
15
14
13
12
11
10
9
8
7
6
5
4
3
2
1
0

**Weight in cubes**

**Objects**

Date

Colouring materials

**2:18 Weight (1)**
Constructing a block graph to represent weight
in non-standard units

# How many?

**1** Complete the empty boxes.

2 legs on a bird.

| 2 + 2 + 2 = 6 |
|---|
| 3 sets of 2. |
| 6 legs altogether. |

3 flowers in a pot.

5 arms on a starfish.

4 legs on a mouse.

6 points on a snowflake.

# Turning patterns

Look at this turning pattern.

**1** Finish and colour these patterns.

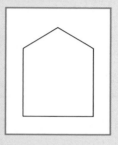 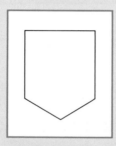   

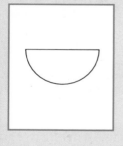 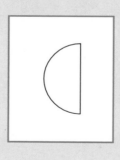 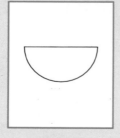  

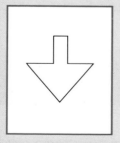 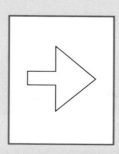  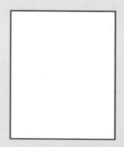 

**2** Make up another turning pattern.
Draw and colour it.

Date        Colouring materials        **2:20 Angles (1)**
Understanding angle as a measurement of turn.

**1** Colour the **even** numbers red.
Colour the **odd** numbers green.

**2** Write the largest **even number**
you know in this space.

# Odd or even? ▪ ▪ ▪ ▪ ▪ ▪ ▪ ▪

**1** Use cubes to make the blocks.
Fill in the empty boxes.

| | number of cubes | odd or even |
|---|---|---|
| | 1 | odd |
| | | |
| | | |
| | | |
| | | |
| | 6 | even |
| | | |
| | | |
| | | |
| | | |

Date      Interlocking cubes

**2:21 Pattern and Sequencing**
Distinguishing odd and even numbers.

14

# Missing blocks

1 Draw the missing blocks.

2 Colour the blocks.

| | small | large |
|---|---|---|
| | △ | |
| | | ◯ |
| | | |

Date

Drawing materials; red
yellow and blue crayons

**2:22 Logic**
Sorting by colour and size.

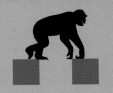

**1** Draw and colour the ice-creams.

| pink | brown | yellow |
|------|-------|--------|
|      |       |        |
|      |       |        |
|      |       |        |

Date

Drawing materials; pink,
brown and yellow crayons

**2:22 Logic**
Sorting by colour and type.

16

# Share the fruit

**1** Share the 8 bananas equally between the two dishes.

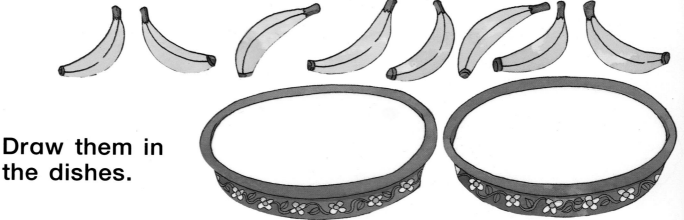

Draw them in the dishes.

**2** Share the 12 apples equally between the three boxes.

Draw them in the boxes.

**3** Share the 20 cherries equally between the five bowls.

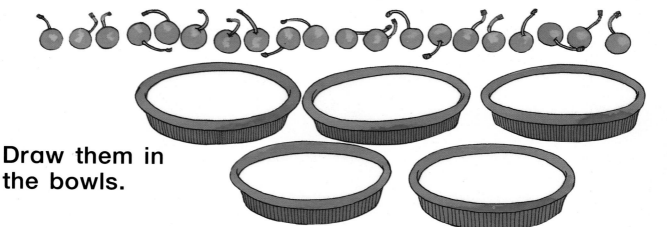

Draw them in the bowls.

Date

Colouring materials

**2:23 Division**
Sharing.

# Making groups

**1** Here are 9 lollipops.

How many hands can each have 3 lollipops?
Draw the lollipops.

**2** Here are 16 candles.

How many cakes can each have 4 candles?
Draw the candles.

**3** Here are 20 buttons.

How many coats can each have 5 buttons?
Draw the buttons.

# Ten in a packet

How many crayons altogether?

There are 10 crayons in each packet

**1** Write the missing numbers.

| | | |
|---|---|---|
| | forty | |
| | | 70 |
| | eighty | |
| | | |
| | | |
| | | |
| | | |
| | | |
| | | |
| | | |

Date

**2:24 Place value 0–100**
Writing tens up to 100.

**1** Draw 10 beads on each lace.

**2** Write numbers in the empty boxes.

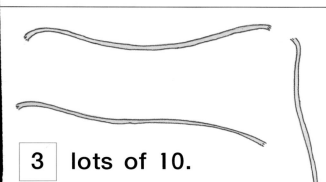

| 3 | lots of 10. |
| 3 | tens make | 30 | . |

| | lots of 10. |
| | tens make | | . |

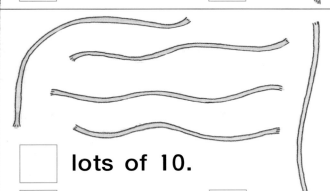

| | lots of 10. |
| | tens make | | . |

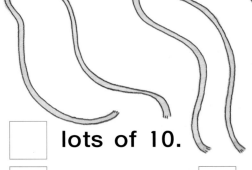

| | lots of 10. |
| | tens make | | . |

**3** Complete the empty boxes.

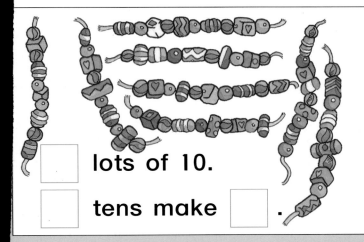

| | lots of 10. |
| | tens make | | . |

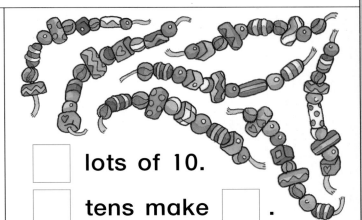

| | lots of 10. |
| | tens make | | . |

Date

**2:24 Place value 0–100**
Making sets of ten up to 100 and writing numerals.

**20**

# Tens and ones ■ ■ ■ ■ ■ ■ ■

**1** Write numbers between 20 and 100 in these boxes.

⬡ ⬡ ⬡ ⬡ ⬡ ⬡ ⬡ ⬡

**2** Colour tens and units for each of your numbers.

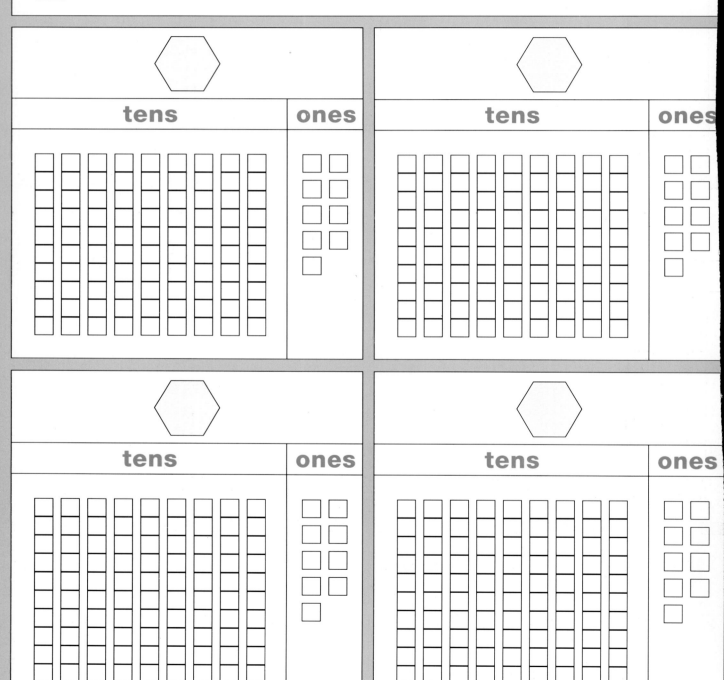

| Date | Writing and colouring materials

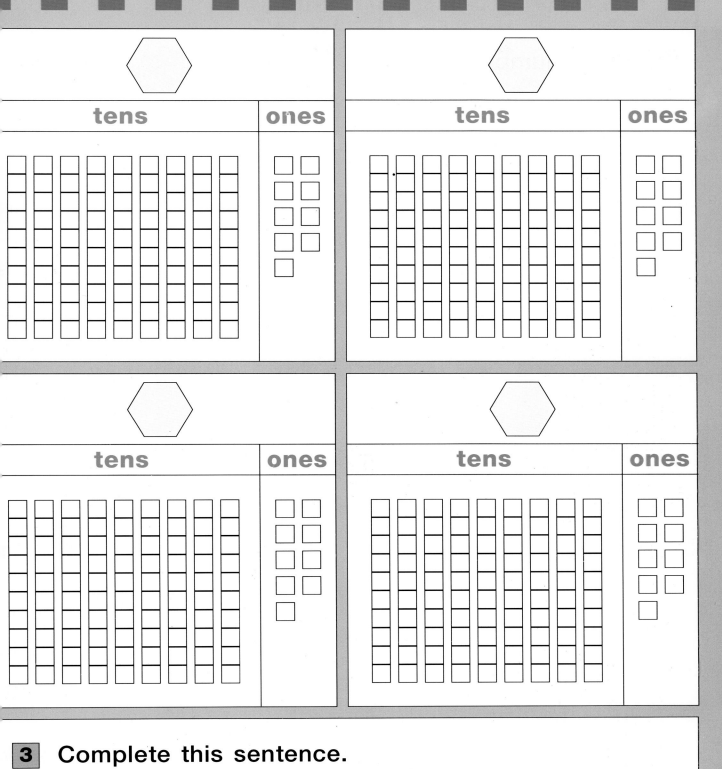

**3** Complete this sentence.

The largest number is , which is ⬜ tens

and ⬜ ones.

Date

**2:24 Place value 0 – 100**
Representing numbers up to 99 as tens and units.

**22**

# Birthdays in our class

Ask your teacher how to make a tally.

| Month | Tally | Total |
|-----------|-------|-------|
| January | | |
| February | | |
| March | | |
| April | | |
| May | | |
| June | | |
| July | | |
| August | | |
| September | | |
| October | | |
| November | | |
| December | | |

**1** Complete these sentences.

There are ☐ more birthdays in _____

than in _____ .

There are ☐ fewer birthdays in _____

than in _____ .

**2** Now complete the graph on the next page.

Date

**2:25 Time (2)**
Using months of the year for a survey.

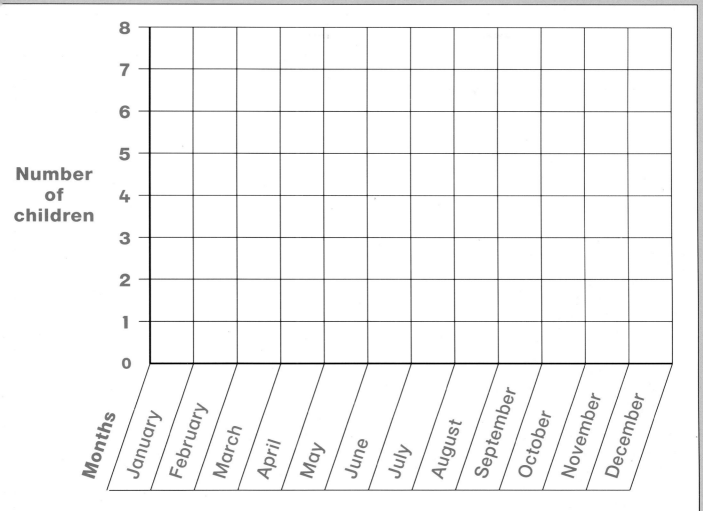

**Number of children**

**Months**

January February March April May June July August September October November December

**1** Write down some things the graph tells you.

# Nets of cubes

**1** Fit tiles together to copy one net at a time.

**2** Fold them to make a cube.

**3** Colour the other two faces of the cube on the page to match what you see.

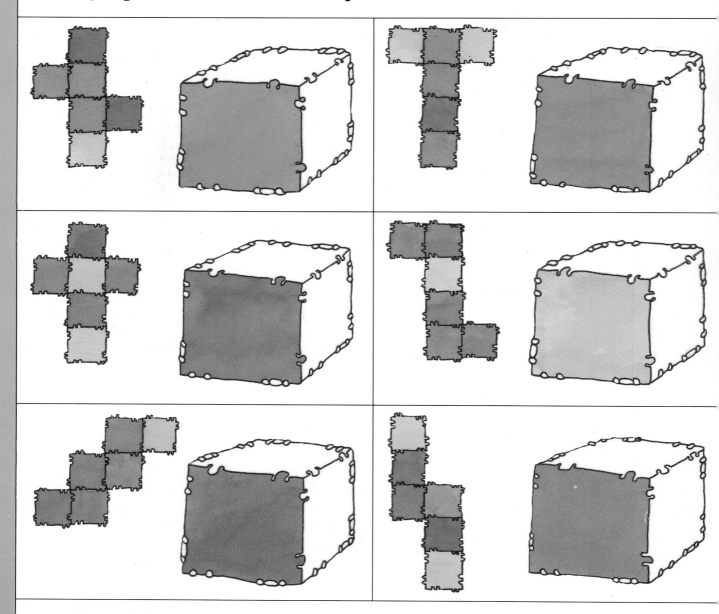

**4** Find and record other ways to make nets of cubes.

Date

Polydron or Clixi square tiles; coloured pencils to match

**2:27 3-D shape (2)**
Making nets for cubes and interpreting them.

# Capacities in litres

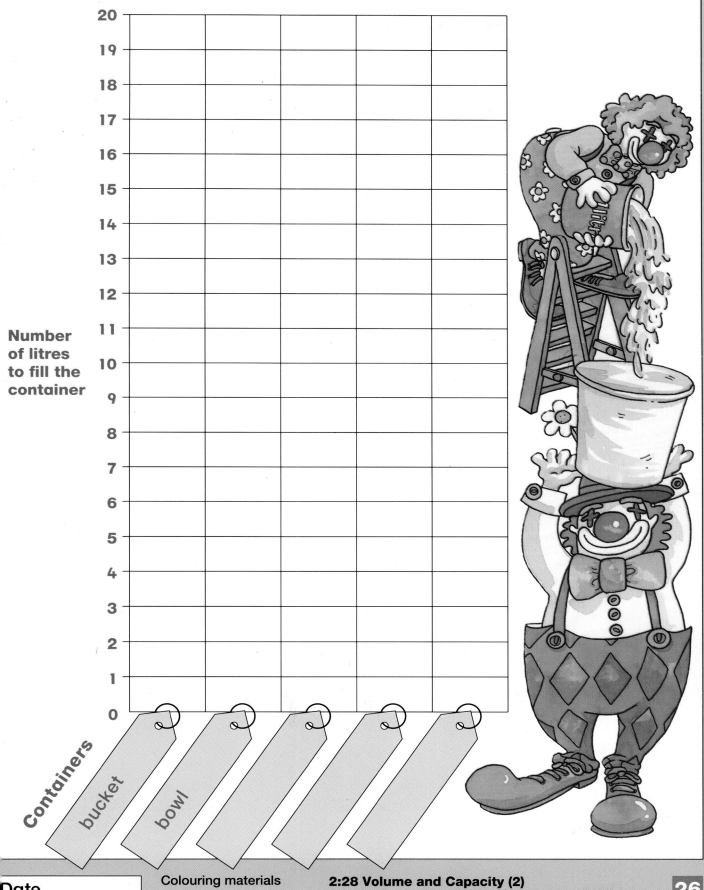

**Number of litres to fill the container**

20
19
18
17
16
15
14
13
12
11
10
9
8
7
6
5
4
3
2
1
0

**Containers**

bucket

bowl

Date

Colouring materials

**2:28 Volume and Capacity (2)**
Constructing a block graph to represent capacities in litres.

26

# Making one litre

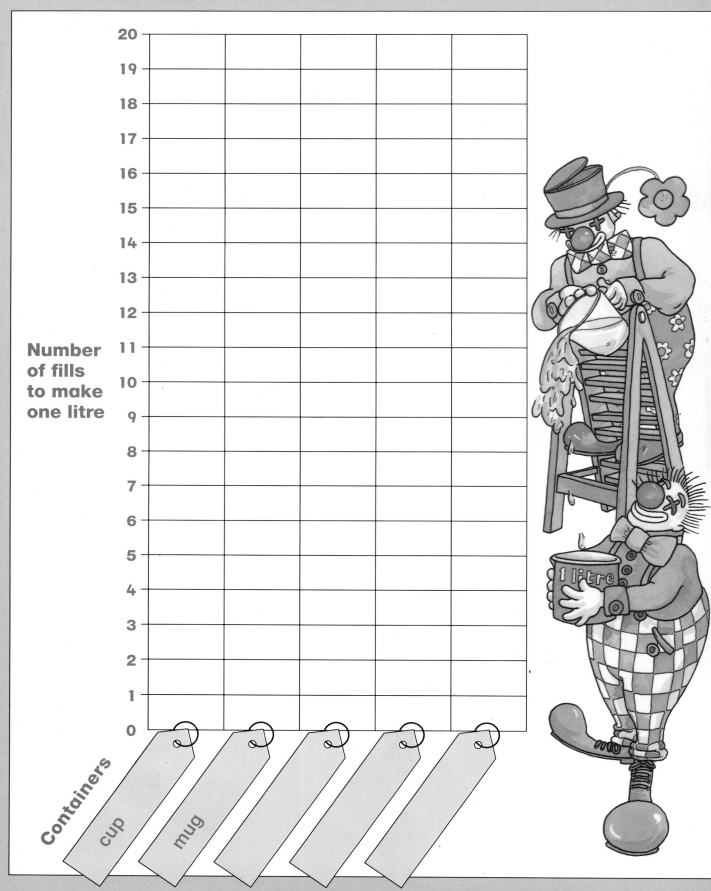

**Number of fills to make one litre**

**Containers**

cup    mug

Date

Colouring materials

**2:28 Volume and Capacity (2)**
Constructing a block graph to represent capacities in litres.

I like hopping forwards best.

I like starting on 6. Find different ways for me.

Whew! We're worn out with all that hopping.

Number line: 0 1 2 3 4 5 6 7 8 9 10 11 12 13 14 15 16 17 18 19 20

| Start at | Hop forward | Land on |
|---|---|---|
| 6 | | |
| 6 | | |
| 6 | | |
| 6 | | |
| 6 | | |
| 6 | | |
| 6 | | |
| 6 | | |
| 6 | | |
| 6 | | |

| Start at | Hop forward | Land on |
|---|---|---|
| 8 | 3 | |
| 11 | 6 | |
| 3 | | 13 |
| | 7 | 11 |
| 9 | | 18 |
| | 2 | 20 |

Use your number line to help you with these.

9 + 7 = ☐

12 + 8 = ☐

13 + ☐ = ☐

☐ + 10 = ☐

Date

**2:29 Addition 0 – 20 (2)**
Counting on to find addition totals up to 20.

28

# Finding totals

You will need a calculator.
You can only use these keys.

Remember to press C after each go to clear your display.

**1** Find as many totals up to 20 as you can.

**2** Write them down.

**3** Cross out the sums that are not correct.

Use objects to help if you want.

3 + 4 + 1 = 8          8 + 5 = 14

9 + 1 + 2 = 13

3 + 7 = 9          2 + 2 + 2 + 2 = 8

7 + 6 = 13

8 + 8 = 16          4 + 5 + 6 = 15

Date

Calculator;
counting objects

2:29 Addition 0 – 20 (2)
Adding involving totals up to 20.

# How many right angles?

You will need          a box          and a pencil.

**1**  Estimate how many right-angled corners there are on your box.

**2**  Number **all** the right-angled corners on your box.

I am numbering right-angled corners on my box.

**3**  Complete these sentences.

I estimated _____ right-angled corners.

I found _____ right-angled corners.

**4**  Compare your results with a friend.

Date

**2:30 Angles (2)**
Recognising right-angled corners on 3-D shapes.

30

## Jungle

How many different animals can you find in the picture on the front cover?

Count how many of each animal.

Colour in the chart to show the numbers.

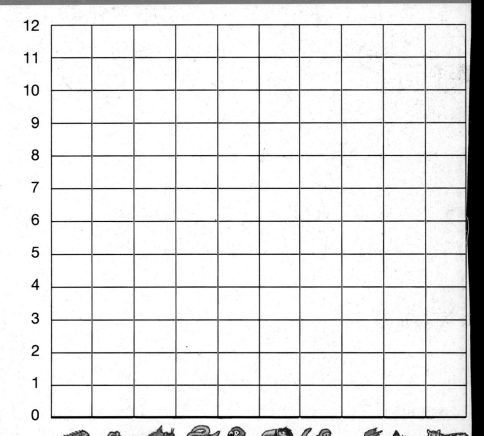

iguanas  frogs  squirrels  snakes  parrots  toucans  monkeys  hummingbirds  butterflies  ocelots

**This book is part of the STEPS mathematics scheme**

Published 1992 by Collins Educational
*An imprint of* HarperCollins*Publishers*
77-85 Fulham Palace Road
London W6 8JB

Reprinted 1993, 1994, 1995

ISBN 0 00 312516-5

© HarperCollins *Publishers* 1992
The authors assert the right to be identified as the authors of this work.

British Library Cataloguing Publication Data
A catalogue record for this book is available from the British Library.
Printed by Scotprint Ltd Musselburgh

**Series Editor:**
Anne Woodman

*Co-Editor:*
Paul Harling

*Consultant Editor:*
Eric Albany

*Project Editor:*
Ann Nimmo

*Illustrations:*
Olivia Bown

*Cover illustration:*
Martin Ursell

*Design and setting:*
Eric Drewery

ISBN 0-00-312516-5

9 780003 125160 >

Collins Educational